Thinking Through Science

Activities from Physics 2

Toni Smith   Carol Tear   Alan Yate

SERIES EDITOR: DAVID EDWARDS

CollinsEducational

An imprint of HarperCollins*Publishers*

Published by Collins Educational
77–85 Fulham Palace Road
Hammersmith
London W6 8JB

First published 1992

British Library Cataloguing in Publication Data

Smith, Toni
 Activities from physics. Bk. 2. – (Thinking through
 science).
 1. Physics
 I. Title. II. Tear, Carol. III. Yate, Alan, IV. Series
 530

ISBN 0-00-327629-5

Typeset by MS Filmsetting Limited, Frome, Somerset
Printed and bound in Hong Kong

Front cover photograph by Eileen Langsley/Supersport
Back cover photograph by Adam Hart-Davis
Book design by Juliet and Charles Snape
Illustration by Juliet Snape, and additional artwork by Sean MacGarry

Contents

About this book   (v)

Unit
1   Candles   2
2   Expand your ideas   4
3   Food irradiation   6
4   In the background   8
5   Sports science   10
6   Time and motion   12
7   Centre of mass   14
8   Counting the cost   16
9   Magnetism from electricity   18
10 On the beach   20
11 National Grid   22
12 The CD revolution   24
13 By word of mouth   26
14 A moving experience   28
15 Keeping warm   30
16 Glowsave versus Wonderwarm   32
17 Tidal energy   34
18 Rock gig   36
19 Eye test   38
20 Cooking and drying with waves   40

Index   43
Acknowledgements   44

About this book

These exercises are about important applications of physics. Some of the information you will have to read—some of it you will have to get from the tables, charts and pictures. You will use this information and what you already know about physics to answer the questions.

Thinking Through Science, Physics 2 will help you to understand some useful ideas in physics. But most of all, we hope that the book will let you enjoy physics—a very important part of our everyday lives.

1 CANDLES

Candle making is becoming a more and more popular pastime.

One method commonly used for making candles is called casting. This involves pouring a mixture of molten wax and stearic acid into a plastic mould. The method is described below.

A wick is threaded through an upturned mould. The mould is then warmed gently in front of a heater or radiator.

A mixture of paraffin wax, stearic acid and a suitable dye is melted together. The mixture is gently poured into the mould and allowed to cool.

When the mixture has solidified, the candle can be released by pouring warm water over the mould.

time (mins)	paraffin wax (°C)	stearic acid (°C)
0	79	82
1	74	77
2	69	74
3	64	71
4	60	70
5	59	70
6	58	70
7	57	69
8	54	66
9	49	61

Temperature control is a very important part of candle making. If the molten wax is too cold, it will begin to set as it is poured into the mould. If it is too hot, the wax will damage the mould and might even cause a fire.

The melting temperatures of the ingredients used to make candles can be found by melting lumps of paraffin wax or stearic acid and recording the temperature as the liquids cool down. Some results are shown in the table.

1. Describe one safety precaution taken when the apparatus used for melting the candle ingredients was chosen.

2. Suggest why the mould is warmed before the molten wax is poured in.

3. Draw a graph to show the cooling curves for the paraffin wax and the stearic acid. Use the same axes for both curves.

4. Write down the freezing point of pure stearic acid. (This is also the melting point.)

5. (a) Describe the melting temperature of paraffin wax.
   (b) Explain why the results show that paraffin wax is not a pure substance.

6. Suggest why it is easier to find the melting temperature of a substance by measuring the temperature of the cooling liquid, rather than the temperature of the solid while it is being heated.

When the paraffin wax or the stearic acid are heated, their particles move more rapidly. In a solid, this increase in movement or **kinetic energy** means that the particles vibrate more. Before a solid can melt, the particles have to separate from one another. Additional energy is needed to make this happen.

If more heat is given to a liquid, the particles move around more quickly – their kinetic energy increases.

A B C D

7. The diagrams represent the arrangement and behaviour of the particles in paraffin wax at various temperatures. Arrange the letters for each of the diagrams in order of increasing temperature.

8. Use the information in the diagrams to explain why paraffin wax contracts as it cools down.

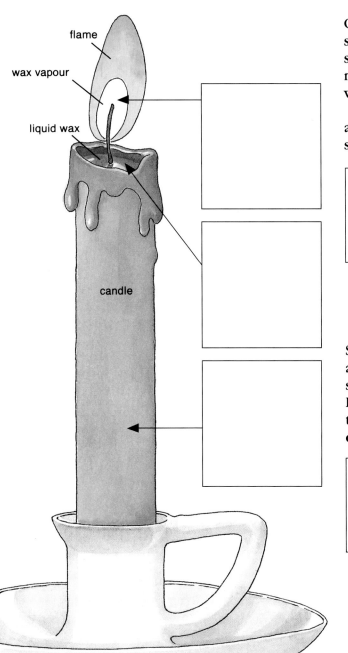

flame

wax vapour

liquid wax

candle

Once a candle has been lit, the heat from the flame is sufficient to melt some of the wax. The molten wax soaks into the wick and up to the centre of the flame, near to where the temperature is highest. Here the wax evaporates to provide fuel for the flame.

In a vapour, the particles are moving very quickly and have enough kinetic energy to remain completely separated from one another.

9. Copy the diagram of the burning candle. Fill in the squares to show the arrangement and behaviour of the wax particles in the three parts of the candle.

Some candles contain an extra ingredient to give them a pleasant smell. As the candle melts, the particles of scent rise up the wick and are released into the room. Because the scent particles are released as a vapour, they spread all around the room – this process is called **diffusion**.

10. Explain why it takes a few minutes for the scent of a candle to fill a room, even though the scent particles are moving relatively quickly.

EXPAND YOUR IDEAS

There is an easier way of loosening the metal top of a Lucozade bottle!

If you hold it under a hot tap, the heat from the water makes the top and the glass expand.

1. Which must expand the most for the same temperature rise – the glass of the bottle or the metal top? Explain your answer.

2. Why would this method not be sensible for the petrol can?

Why do substances expand?

There is a very important theory which helps us to understand how substances behave – it is called the particle kinetic theory.

The word 'kinetic' means movement. An important difference between a solid and a liquid is to do with how freely the particles within them can move.

In solids like the bottle top, the particles move about a fixed position. If the solid is heated, the particles move more about their fixed positions, and take up more space.

In a liquid like Lucozade the particles are not fixed in position – they move about and bump into each other. The hotter the liquid, the faster the particles move about.

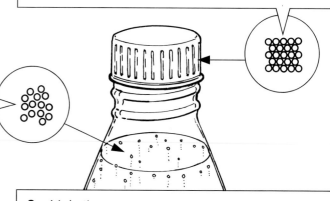

But what has all this got to do with expansion?

Tom's theory

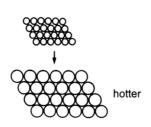

hotter

"I think that as a solid is heated, the particles get bigger. The more you heat something, the bigger they get. Is this why solids expand as they get hot?"

Sophie's theory

hotter

"My idea is that as a solid is heated, the particles vibrate more. The more they vibrate, the more they push apart. Could this be why solids expand when they are heated?"

3. Explain why Sophie's ideas about expansion fit in with the particle kinetic theory better than Tom's.

4. The particles in a gas move about freely. The hotter the gas, the faster the particles move. Use these ideas to explain why the sides of a plastic bottle get pushed out when the gas inside is heated.

When the switch is in the 'on' position, the small spring is pushed against a thermostat. The thermostat is a 'bimetal' strip – it is made of two different metals, such as steel and brass, which expand by different amounts. Because the two metals are fixed together and one metal expands more than another, the strip bends when it gets hot.

5. Copy out and complete these sentences.

A thermostat is made with a _____ strip. This _____ when it is heated because one of the metals _____ more than the other.

6. Brass expands more than steel. Draw a diagram to show how the strip will bend when it is heated.

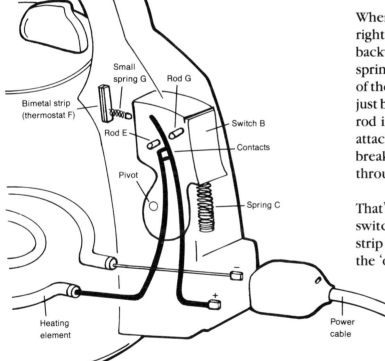

When the kettle boils, the thermostat bends to the right and pushes the small spring and the switch backwards. The switch jumps back, pulled by another spring. There are two rods sticking out from the side of the switch, one just in front of the contacts and one just behind them. As the switch moves backwards, the rod in front of the contacts catches a piece of metal attached to one of them and pushes them apart. This breaks the circuit, and the electricity stops flowing through the heating element.

That's why you can't keep the contacts together to switch on the kettle if the kettle is hot – the bimetal strip is still bent and keeps pushing the switch back to the 'off' position.

7. Copy the flow diagrams below. Use the letters on the diagram of the kettle to fill in the spaces in the boxes. The first flow diagram is what happens when the kettle is switched on.

switch pushed forward	→	compresses small spring	→	against thermostat	→	rod moves forward	→	allows contacts to come together
LETTER ☐	→	☐	→	☐	→	☐	→	☐

CIRCUIT COMPLETE – KETTLE HEATS UP

When the kettle boils ...

thermostat bends	→	pushes small spring	→	switch pulled back by spring	→	rod moves backwards
LETTER ☐	→	☐	→	☐	→	☐

CIRCUIT BROKEN – KETTLE SWITCHES OFF

FOOD IRRADIATION

Did you see that television programme last night? Going to spray our food with that nuclear radiation – I don't know, what ever next?

Yes I saw that. Supposed to make the food last longer – or so they say. I wouldn't touch radioactive food, let alone eat the stuff. Everyone knows that radiation is dangerous – you're always hearing about leaks and things.

Now there's an idea for the school magazine . . .

RADIOACTIVITY

Most elements are made from atoms which are stable – but some atoms are unstable, and break up into smaller pieces of their own accord. This is a quite natural process which is called radioactive decay.

When atoms break up, radiation is released. There are three different types of this radiation: alpha (α), beta (β), and gamma (γ). Alpha and beta radiation are streams of tiny particles from within the atoms. Gamma radiation is a wave like those used in X-ray machines and for radio transmissions.

The radiations released during radioactive decay have a lot of energy, and this is why they can be both useful and dangerous.

If the radiation has enough energy, it can break up molecules. Radiation that can do this is called ionising radiation. High energy alpha, beta and gamma radiation are examples of ionising radiation. They can penetrate body tissues, and damage the long, complicated molecules which store the instructions for making new cells. This can cause diseases such as cancer and leukaemia. If the damage occurs in a sex cell, offspring can have birth defects.

By contrast, because radiation is so energetic, it can be used to kill unwanted cells, such as those which grow out of control to form a cancer tumour. Doses of gamma rays are fired at the cancerous tumour until it is destroyed.

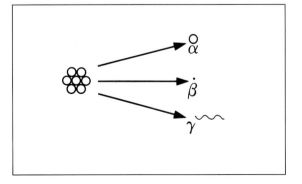

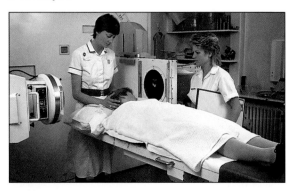

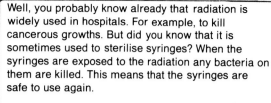

Can you give me any information about food irradiation?

Can you tell me how it works?

Well, you probably know already that radiation is widely used in hospitals. For example, to kill cancerous growths. But did you know that it is sometimes used to sterilise syringes? When the syringes are exposed to the radiation any bacteria on them are killed. This means that the syringes are safe to use again.

The same principle is used to preserve food. For example, in some countries where transportation is slow, grain is irradiated to kill the bacteria which make the grain decay.

But can radiation make food that has gone off safe to eat?

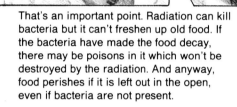

That's an important point. Radiation can kill bacteria but it can't freshen up old food. If the bacteria have made the food decay, there may be poisons in it which won't be destroyed by the radiation. And anyway, food perishes if it is left out in the open, even if bacteria are not present.

NUTRITECH INDUSTRIES

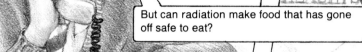

The case for food irradiation

Food irradiation involves exposing food to high energy gamma rays. The radiation kills any harmful bacteria which cause food to decay, but …

the food does NOT become radio-active!

The result is that food lasts longer and so less goes to waste.

Did you know …

American and Russian space crews have been eating irradiated food since 1975!

10 countries already allow irradiated food to be sold.

In Miami, where it can be very hot, irradiated fruit sells better than untreated fruit.

Not all foods can be treated with radiation – seafood goes black and tomatoes go soft. More research is being carried out, but to date, there seems to be no good reason for not eating irradiated food.

NUTRITECH … the company that cares for your food.

This leaflet has some interesting information in it.

YOUR TASK

Write an article of about 750 words for your school magazine. The article should include a catchy title, an explanation of what food irradiation is, an explanation of why people are suspicious of radiation, and a description of the advantages of and concerns about food irradiation.

IN THE BACKGROUND

A report from the power station said 'The radiation from the leak will only produce a slight rise above the background radiation. It will be difficult to detect such a small increase. However, any leak is a cause for concern, and an immediate investigation has begun.'

The cloud is moving northwards, and is not expected to affect any other countries.

How can they be sure? Suppose it is as bad as Chernobyl?

What is background radiation? How do you measure it?

Background radiation is radiation which is around all the time. It comes from radioactive substances in some types of rock, and from outer space. It is higher in Scotland and Cornwall because of the type of rocks there.

We measured the background radiation at school yesterday – perhaps we should keep measuring it for the rest of the week and see if this leak makes any difference.

The computer counts the number of pulses for 10 minutes, then the total is divided by 10 to get the average number of pulses in 1 minute. This gives the average count rate. The computer does this every 12 hours and records the average count rate each time.

It's difficult to see a pattern in numbers. We should draw a chart.

This is a Geiger counter. Every time it detects radiation entering the tube it sends an electric pulse to the counter. The number of pulses in a minute is called the count rate.

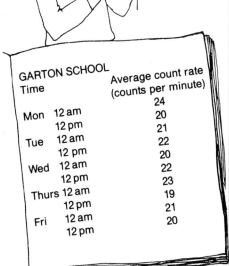

GARTON SCHOOL

Time		Average count rate (counts per minute)
Mon	12 am	24
	12 pm	20
Tue	12 am	21
	12 pm	22
Wed	12 am	20
	12 pm	22
Thurs	12 am	23
	12 pm	19
Fri	12 am	21
	12 pm	20

1. What is meant by (a) background radiation (b) count rate?

2. Draw a bar chart of average count rate against time for these results.

3. Which of these statements best describes your bar chart:
   (a) the height of the bars gradually goes up
   (b) the height of the bars gradually goes down
   (c) the height of the bars is random, which means there is no pattern?

4. Explain what would be happening to the level of background radiation
   (a) if the height of the bars went up
   (b) if the height of the bars went down
   (c) if the heights of the bars were random.

5. From the graph, did radiation from the power station appear to affect the school?

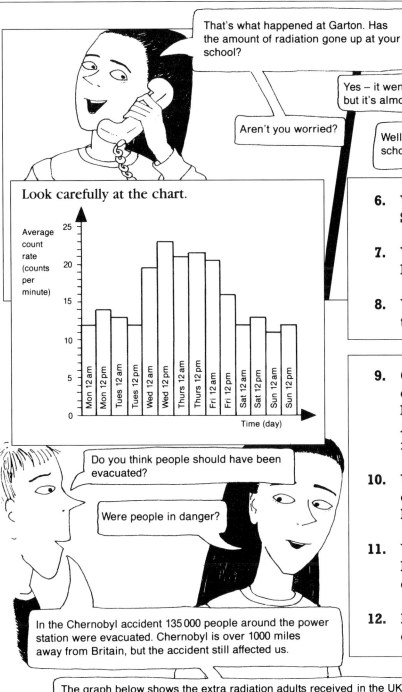

Look carefully at the chart.

6. When did the radiation reach Alminster School?

7. When had the radiation fallen almost to the background radiation again?

8. When did the radiation at the school reach the maximum value?

9. Compare the background radiation in the chart you plotted for Garton, and the highest radiation level in the chart for Alminster. Which place had the highest radiation level, and when did it occur?

10. What was the earliest time at which you could know what the maximum radiation level caused by the leak had been?

11. Will everywhere around the power station have the same level of increased radiation due to the leak? Explain your answer.

12. In your opinion should people have been evacuated? Explain your answer.

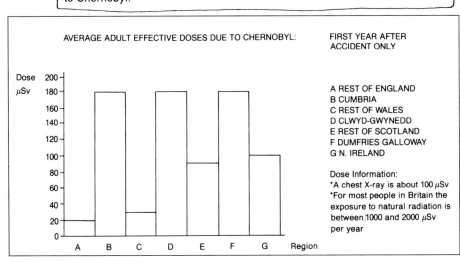

The graph below shows the extra radiation adults received in the UK due to Chernobyl.

AVERAGE ADULT EFFECTIVE DOSES DUE TO CHERNOBYL: FIRST YEAR AFTER ACCIDENT ONLY

A REST OF ENGLAND
B CUMBRIA
C REST OF WALES
D CLWYD-GWYNEDD
E REST OF SCOTLAND
F DUMFRIES GALLOWAY
G N. IRELAND

Dose Information:
*A chest X-ray is about 100 μSv
*For most people in Britain the exposure to natural radiation is between 1000 and 2000 μSv per year

13. Which region do you live in?

14. What was the average adult dose there?

15. Why does the graph say "first year after accident only"?

16. Was the dose in your area equivalent to
(a) less than one X-ray,
(b) more than one X-ray,
(c) more than two X-rays?

5
SPORTS SCIENCE

Every sport we do MOVES something. In order to move anything a FORCE is needed. Forces are measured in NEWTONS (N).

Running – you move forward because of the PUSHING force of your feet against the ground (friction).

THRUST

FRICTION

The THRUST force is bigger than the friction – so the athlete moves forward.

1. Write down what happens when there is little (or no) friction between your feet and the ground. (Think about trying to run on ice.)

2. What happens when the force of friction is greater than the thrust force you could provide? (Think about trying to run in thick mud.)

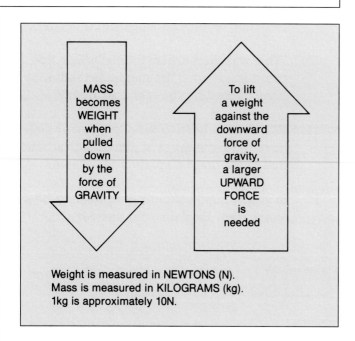

MASS becomes WEIGHT when pulled down by the force of GRAVITY

To lift a weight against the downward force of gravity, a larger UPWARD FORCE is needed

Weight is measured in NEWTONS (N).
Mass is measured in KILOGRAMS (kg).
1kg is approximately 10N.

THE BAR HAS A MASS OF 10kg

30 kg

30 kg

MY MASS IS 90 kg

3. What is the total mass of the weight-lifter and weights?

4. What is the weight of the weight-lifter?

5. How much do the weights weigh?

6. How much force would another weight-lifter have to use to lift our weight-lifter and the weights?

7. Imagine you are trying to stop the rugby player with the ball. Would it be harder or easier to stop him if he was lighter, but still moving with the same velocity?

8. Give a reason for your answer to question 7.

9. Draw a matchstick picture of the rugby player with the ball. Use arrows to show at least three forces in action. Label the forces.

1

2

3

4

10. Look at the first picture of the bowler in action. Draw a matchstick person picture to show one downward force and two forces acting in opposite directions. Use a large arrow to show large forces and a small arrow to show small forces.

11. Which pictures show the bowler exerting a force on the ground?

12. How can the bowler increase the force on the ground to get a better grip for the run-up?

13. In which picture of the bowler is the velocity of the ball
    (a) the least
    (b) the most?

14. Would the bowler have to use more or less force if the ball was a greater mass (for the same velocity)?

15. Draw a picture of the tennis racket. Show on your picture how the strings would change shape when the racket hits the ball.

16. Name two forces which propel the ball forward.

17. What is the effect of hitting the ball with a heavier racket?

6

TIME AND MOTION

Janet and Riyad both work for the same company – Carryaway Couriers Ltd. At the depot they pick up directions for their next delivery.

1. Write down two reasons why Carryaway Couriers like to use motorbikes as well as vans for their deliveries.

2. Graph A settles down to a speed of about 20 m/s and B to a speed of about 10 m/s. Use the graph to estimate how long it takes each vehicle to reach these speeds.

   The graphs show the speeds of the two vehicles leaving the depot.

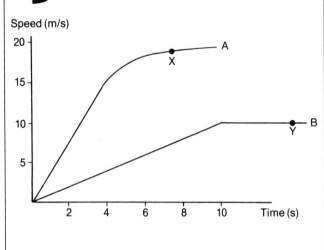

3. Which graph (A or B) do you think shows the bike leaving the depot? Explain your answer.

4. Look at the shape of the two graphs. Which shows the highest **acceleration**? Give a reason for your answer. Suggest what is happening to the speeds of the vehicles at X and Y.

Acceleration is calculated using this equation:

$$\text{ACCELERATION} = \frac{\text{Change in speed (m/s)}}{\text{time taken (s)}}$$

5. The units of acceleration are metres per second per second (or metres per second squared, m/s^2). Using your answer to question 4 and the equation, work out the accelerations of both the bike and the van. Copy the acceleration equation into your book.

One disadvantage of having a vehicle capable of rapid acceleration is that it is easier to break the speed limit. This happened to Janet one day. She and Riyad left the depot together and as Janet was in a hurry she sped off. Two minutes later she passed a police officer. She was stopped for doing 10km/h over the speed limit.

THAT BIKE MUST BE GOING FASTER THAN THE 100 km/h LIMIT!

6. What speed was Janet doing as she passed the police officer?

7. Work out her AVERAGE acceleration. Why is 'average' important here?

8. The van passes by 2 minutes later as Janet and the police officer are talking. Work out the average acceleration of the van.

9. Both the van and the bike have the same size of engine. Why should the bike be able to accelerate faster than the van?

10. Janet's friend Joe has a 450cc bike. Would Joe be able to accelerate faster than Riyad's van? Explain your answer.

12

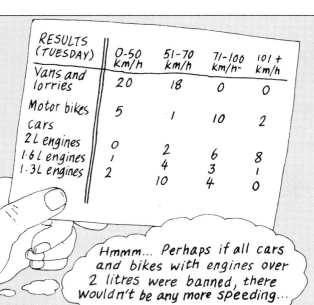

RESULTS (TUESDAY)	0-50 km/h	51-70 km/h	71-100 km/h	101+ km/h
Vans and lorries	20	18	0	0
Motor bikes	5	1	10	2
Cars				
2L engines	0	2	6	8
1.6L engines	1	4	3	1
1.3L engines	2	10	4	0

Hmmm... Perhaps if all cars and bikes with engines over 2 litres were banned, there wouldn't be any more speeding...

At the end of the day the police officer looks at the record of the speeds of all the passing traffic.

11. Draw a bar chart to represent these results. Use a different colour for each category of vehicle.

12. Suggest why more 2 litre cars were stopped than 1.3 litre cars.

13. Explain why the police officer's idea is not very good.

This is a speed-time graph for Riyad's journey.

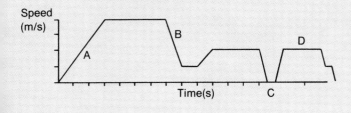

14. Describe what is happening in terms of speeds and accelerations at A B C and D.

15. Calculate the acceleration at D and the deceleration at B.

16. Riyad was given the map shown below. Use the speed–time graph to work out which route he took. Write down his directions clearly explaining your answer.

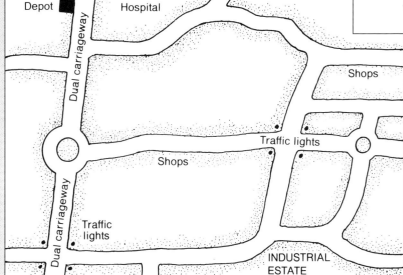

JANET: RIDER 1   9 September

Letters and documents to Mr Smith (solicitor) at 6 BRASS ROAD, RADMORE TOWN.

Left turn out of depot onto dual carriageway for 2km. Turn left at the roundabout, into village of Bradcote. Go through centre of village and take the left after the school. Go up the steep hill for 1km, then turn right. It is signposted to Radmore. Go over the railway crossing into the town. After the pedestrian crossing, the solicitor's office is the second on the right.

17. Now draw a similar speed–time graph for Janet's journey. Remember she was stopped by the police for some time. Here are the directions for her delivery.

7

CENTRE OF MASS

THIS IS A STABLE POSITION:
a slight movement will not cause toppling over as the centre of mass will not be displaced outside the base area.

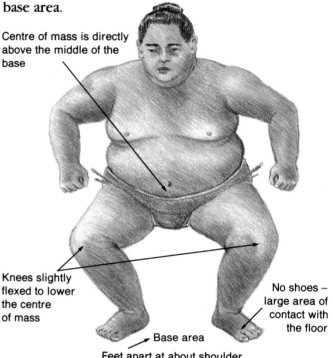

Centre of mass is directly above the middle of the base

Knees slightly flexed to lower the centre of mass

No shoes – large area of contact with the floor

Base area

Feet apart at about shoulder width, to increase size of base area

1. Objects behave as if all their weight acts at one point. The position of this point affects whether the object will BALANCE or TOPPLE OVER. What is this point called?

2. Use the information about the sumo wrestler to make up your own scientific definition of
   (a) A STABLE OBJECT
   (b) AN UNSTABLE OBJECT.

3. Look at these two pictures of judo players. Which one shows the red belt about to topple over? Explain your answer using the words 'centre of mass' and 'base area'.

4. Will she fall?
   Explain your answer in scientific terms.

THIS IS AN UNSTABLE POSITION:
a slight movement to the left or right will cause the unicyclist to topple as the centre of mass will then fall outside the base area.

Top heavy – so the centre of mass is high

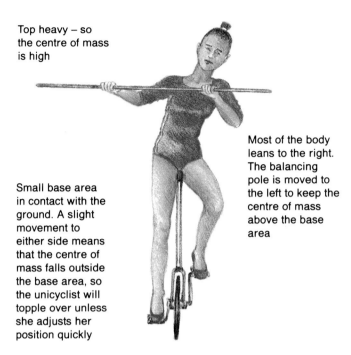

Small base area in contact with the ground. A slight movement to either side means that the centre of mass falls outside the base area, so the unicyclist will topple over unless she adjusts her position quickly

Most of the body leans to the right. The balancing pole is moved to the left to keep the centre of mass above the base area

The following sentences have mistakes. Rewrite them so that they are correct. Include the underlined words in your correct sentences.

6. *The centre of mass is always half way up an object.*

7. *The wider the feet, the more stable a person is.*

8. *Toppling occurs if the centre of mass is too high*

9. *A racing car is stable because it has 4 wheels.*

10. *A heavy long pole is used in balancing acts because it increases the overall weight.*

11. *A double decker bus is stable because it is tall.*

12. *If the centre of mass falls outside the base area then the object will spin rapidly.*

13. *To knock someone over you have to 'break their balance' which means lowering their centre of mass.*

5. Explain carefully why this man carries a pole.

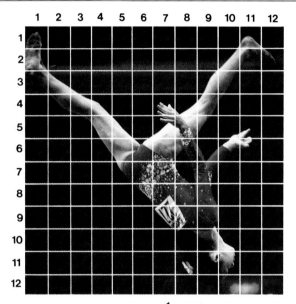

	1	2	3	4	5	6	7	8	9	10	11	12

SPOT THE CENTRE OF MASS COMPETITION

Look at this photograph of Olympic competitor Inoue Asako performing one of her famous somersaults.

Where is her centre of mass?

On a postcard, to reach us no later than 23rd April, tell us which square you think her centre of mass is in. As a tie-breaker, complete this sentence in under 20 words:

THE POSITION OF THE CENTRE OF MASS IS ......
....
BECAUSE ....

14. When objects turn, they usually do so round their centre of mass. Trace the outline of the gymnast and mark on your diagram
   (a) the centre of mass and
   (b) the direction in which she is turning.

8

COUNTING THE COST

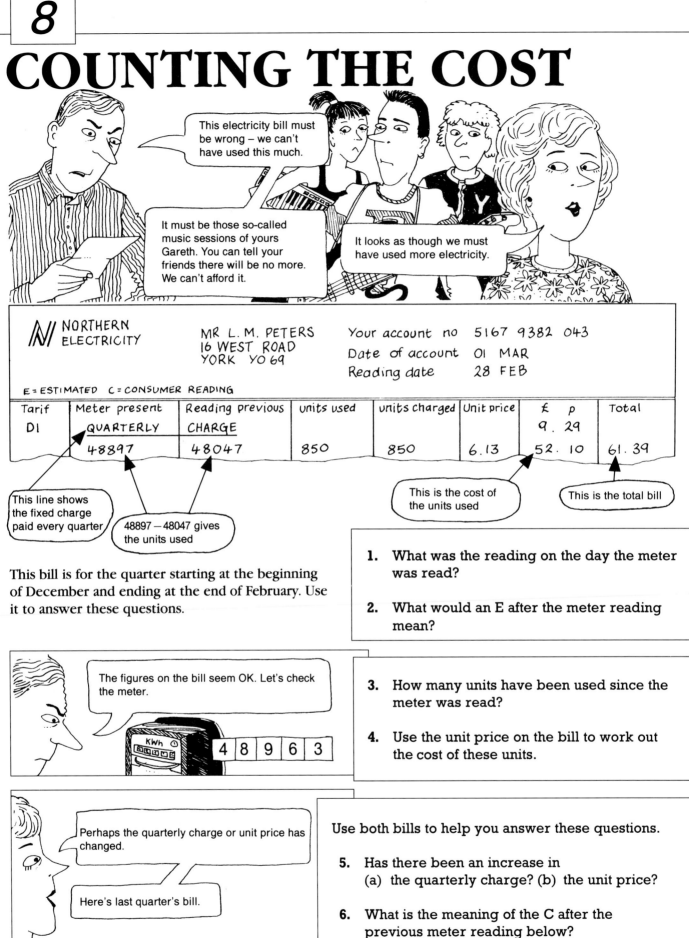

"This electricity bill must be wrong – we can't have used this much."

"It must be those so-called music sessions of yours Gareth. You can tell your friends there will be no more. We can't afford it."

"It looks as though we must have used more electricity."

NORTHERN ELECTRICITY

MR L. M. PETERS
16 WEST ROAD
YORK YO 69

Your account no 5167 9382 043
Date of account 01 MAR
Reading date 28 FEB

E = ESTIMATED   C = CONSUMER READING

Tarif	Meter present	Reading previous	units used	units charged	Unit price	£ p	Total
D1	QUARTERLY	CHARGE				9 . 29	
	48897	48047	850	850	6.13	52 . 10	61.39

This line shows the fixed charge paid every quarter

48897 − 48047 gives the units used

This is the cost of the units used

This is the total bill

This bill is for the quarter starting at the beginning of December and ending at the end of February. Use it to answer these questions.

1. What was the reading on the day the meter was read?

2. What would an E after the meter reading mean?

"The figures on the bill seem OK. Let's check the meter."

KWh 4 8 9 6 3

3. How many units have been used since the meter was read?

4. Use the unit price on the bill to work out the cost of these units.

"Perhaps the quarterly charge or unit price has changed."

"Here's last quarter's bill."

Use both bills to help you answer these questions.

5. Has there been an increase in
   (a) the quarterly charge? (b) the unit price?

6. What is the meaning of the C after the previous meter reading below?

Tarif	Meter present	Reading previous	units used	units charged	Unit price	£ p	Total
D1	QUARTERLY	CHARGE				9 . 29	
	48047	47392C	655	655	6.13	40 . 15	49.44

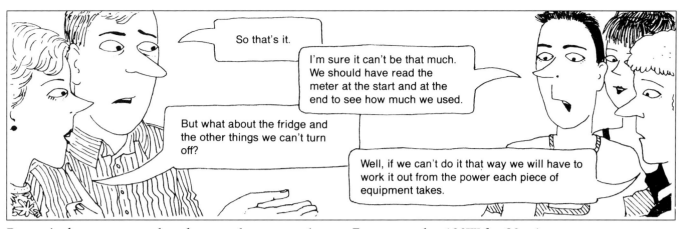

Power is the energy used each second, so to work out how much energy was used we need to know how long each instrument was used for.

This is the plate from the back of Paul's guitar amplifier. Here is the power rating in watts.

220–240V
100W
50Hz

Energy used = 100W for 30 mins
Change this to kilowatts (kW) and hours to get the units
in kilowatt hours
$= 0.1\text{kW} \times 0.5\text{h}$
$= 0.05$ units

1kW = 1000W

7. Here are information plates for the other equipment and the time each was used for. Work out how many kilowatt hours each one used.

220–240V ac 50Hz 150W	240V ac 240W	240V ac 120W	240V ac 80W	240V ac 50Hz 200W	240V ac 180W
Keyboard amplifier 2 hours	Drum kit amplifier 2 hours	Multitrack tape recorder 4 hours	Mixing desk 2 hours	Bass amplifier 2 hours	Drum kit 2 hours

8. Add up all the kilowatt hours to find the total electricity the group used.

START
4 9 0 1 3

END
4 9 0 1 8

9. From these meter readings, how many units of electricity were used during the practice session?

10. How much does this many units cost?

11. From your answers to questions 8 and 9 work out how much electricity was used in the house during the practice session by items which were on all the time (like the fridge).

12. Which of these new items used the most units in a week?

13. What was the total extra units used by these new appliances in a week?

14. Work out by how much these extra units each week increase the cost for the quarter.

15. Which item should the family stop using to save the most money?

9

MAGNETISM FROM ELECTRICITY

FACT FILE
MAGNETISM FROM ELECTRICITY

(i) When an electric current flows in a wire, a magnetic field is produced.

(ii) If the same wire is wound into a coil and the same current flows through it, a stronger magnetic field is produced.

(iii) The larger the current of electricity, the stronger the magnetic field will be.

(iv) The more turns there are in the coil, the stronger the magnetic field will be.

(v) The direction of the current tells us at which end of the coil the north and south poles will be.

(vi) A north pole will repel a north pole, and a south pole will repel a south pole.

(vii) North and south poles will be attracted to each other.

(viii) The repulsion and attraction of two magnetic poles can be used to provide motion.

(ix) Magnetic fields produced by electricity can control beams of electrons.

(x) Beams of electrons make the pictures on television and computer screens.

(xi) The vibration in a loudspeaker is made by magnetic poles attracting and repelling.

A FOOD MIXER

B TAPE RECORDER

G WASHING MACHINE

K AUTOMATIC CAMERA

H VACUUM CLEANER

N SHAVER

O HAIR DRIER

T RADIO

U EXTRACTOR FAN

V TELEVISION

W VIDEO RECORDER

X HEDGE TRIMMERS

C STRIMMER

D SEWING MACHINE

I FAN HEATER

J RECORD AND TAPE SYSTEM

L ELECTRIC DRILL

M ELECTRIC MOWER

P MODEL RACING CAR GAME

Q PAINT STRIPPER

R VIDEO CAMERA

S MICROWAVE OVEN

Y REFRIGERATOR

Z ELECTRIC FAN

E PERSONAL STEREO

F MICRO COMPUTER
VDU
DISK DRIVE

1. Electric motors use the magnetic effect of electricity. Write down the letters of the items which contain electric motors.

2. Some items shown on this page contain motors which can operate at more than one speed. Write down the letters of these items.

3. Choose two statements from the fact file which best describe how the items in question 2 work.

4. Some of the items on this page use magnetism from electricity to move in more than one direction. Write down the letters of the items which do this.

5. Choose the statement from the fact file which best describes how the items in question 4 could operate.

6. Write down the letters of the items which contain loudspeakers.

7. In loudspeakers there is a part that vibrates to make sound. Choose the statement from the fact file which best describes how the part is made to vibrate.

8. Write down the letters of the items which use magnetism to control beams of electrons. Use the fact file to help you.

9. Which statement from the fact file best describes how the volume of a sound produced by a radio or tape recorder could be increased.

ON THE BEACH

This car has arrived at the seaside after a long journey. The tyres are hot with a temperature of 35°C. The pressure inside the tyres is 3×10^5 N/m².

1. What is the temperature of the tyres measured in Kelvin?

After an afternoon by the beach the temperature of the tyres has fallen to 20°C.

2. What is the new temperature of the tyres measured in Kelvin?

3. What is the new pressure in the tyres? Assume the volume of the tyres stays constant.

4. Explain why motorists are advised not to check tyre pressures immediately after a long journey.

When the cyclist arrives at the beach, the pressure in the front tyre of the bike is 6×10^5 N/m² and the temperature of the tyre is 30°C.

5. Calculate the pressure in the tyre when it has cooled to 21°C. Assume the volume stays constant and remember to change both the temperatures to Kelvin.

If the cyclist puts her finger over the end of the pump it is difficult to push the handle because she is compressing the air in the pump.

6. Do you think compressing the air in the pump will increase or decrease the temperature of the air?

7. Before the air in the pump is compressed the pressure is 1.00×10^5 N/m², the temperature is 20°C and the volume is 5.30×10^{-5} m³. After compression the new volume is 4.40×10^{-5} m³ and the pressure is 1.21×10^5 N/m². What is the new temperature?

Check that your answer agrees with your answer to question 6.

This lilo is 2m long, 50cm wide and 10cm high.

8. What is the volume of the lilo in m³?

THE GAS LAW

For a fixed mass of gas:

$$\frac{p_1 V_1}{T_1} = \frac{p_2 V_2}{T_2}$$

where p = pressure (units N/m²)
T = temperature (units K)
V = volume (units m³)

The value of temperature in Kelvin is found by adding 273 to the Celsius reading.

On the beach the temperature of the children's armbands is 25°C, but in the sea the temperature falls to 13°C. The volume of the armbands stays constant (0.001 m³).

The diver releases a bubble of air at the sea bed. The pressure of the water there is 3×10^5 N/m². The volume of the bubble is 4.19×10^{-6} m³.

10. What will the volume of the bubble be just before it reaches the surface of the water? Assume the temperature stays constant. The air pressure is 1×10^5 N/m².

11. The pressure in the inflatable dinghy is 1.3×10^5 N/m² at a temperature of 21°C. At night the temperature falls to 5°C. What is the new pressure in the dinghy? Assume the volume stays the same.

12. If the pressure inside the armbands on the beach is 1.20×10^5 N/m², what is the pressure while they are in the sea? (Don't forget to convert temperatures into Kelvin.)

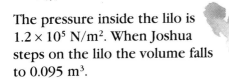

13. The beach ball has a volume of 0.015 m³, a temperature of 21°C and a pressure inside of 2×10^5 N/m². During the game the ball falls into the sea where the temperature is 13°C. If the volume is still 0.015 m³, what is the new pressure inside the ball?

The pressure inside the lilo is 1.2×10^5 N/m². When Joshua steps on the lilo the volume falls to 0.095 m³.

9. What is the new pressure in the lilo? Assume the temperature stays the same.

NATIONAL GRID

The map shows the location of power stations in Britain.

1. How many different types of power station are there?

2. Which type appears to be the most common?

Start

The first commercial wind power station in Britain was built on the island of Orkney.

3. What are the advantages of placing the windpower generator on a largely uninhabited island?

Dounreay is an experimental nuclear power station.

4. How many other nuclear power stations are there in Britain?

5. Describe the similarities in the locations of all the nuclear power stations.

6. Why are there none built near large towns?

Hydroelectric power (HEP) stations are mostly built in mountainous areas like Scotland and Wales.

7. Why are they built in these areas?

8. Why have so many small HEP stations been built instead of one or two big ones?

Pumped storage stations are HEP stations which can pump water back up into the reservoir when the demand for electricity is low. The water then runs down again, generating more electricity, when demand is high.

9. How many pumped storage stations are there?

Key

●	Coal fired stations	◑	Coal/Oil power stations
●	Oil power stations	▲	Diesel power stations
▲	Nuclear power stations	◐	Coal/Gas power stations
○	Gas turbine power stations	△	Wind power stations
●	Hydroelectric power stations	◓	Oil/Gas stations
▲	Pumped storage power stations	◖	Coalfields
		●	Cities

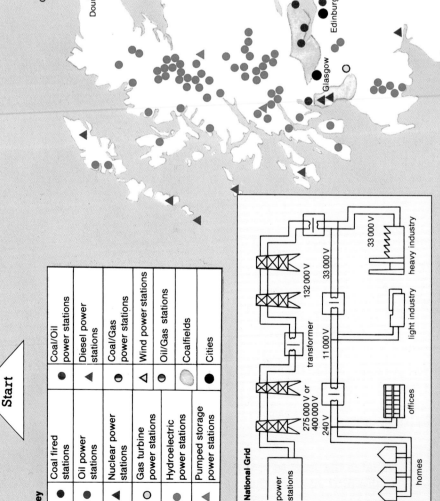

National Grid

Coal fired power stations are built close to supplies of coal for their fuel, and water for their cooling towers.

10. Suggest how coal could be transported from the mines to the power stations.

11. Describe the location of most oil and gas fired power stations.

12. Give a reason why oil and gas fired power stations are built in these locations.

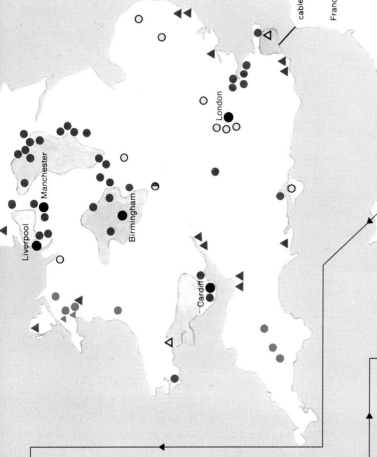

cable

France

London

Manchester

Liverpool

Birmingham

Cardiff

An undersea electricity cable connects the UK to France so that electricity can be bought or sold to the French.

Most people live in towns, where a lot of electricity is used. Electricity must be transported from the power stations, which are often in remote areas, to the homes and factories where it is needed. Electricity needs to be generated at the time we want to use it, but power stations take a long time to start up.

13. Describe two ways of meeting a sudden increase in demand for electricity. (Hint: both are shown on the map.)

Some people think that using lots of different ways of generating electricity is a good idea, rather than relying on one source of power.

20. Give one disadvantage of using only:
(a) Wind power stations
(b) Nuclear power stations
(c) Coal fired stations
(d) Oil power stations.

The **National Grid** connects all the power stations to the users. Electricity is carried in either overhead cables supported by pylons, or in underground cables. The electrical energy supplied each second can be increased in two ways—by increasing the current flowing through the cables or by increasing the voltage across the cables.

14. What happens to wires if a high current flows in them?

15. How can the current in the cables be reduced, while still supplying the same energy each second?

16. Explain why connecting all electricity users and power stations to the National Grid is an advantage:
(a) If a local power station has to be shut down,
(b) If all the inhabitants of one town are warned to boil their water during a pollution scare.

17. What voltages does the National Grid use?

18. What voltage is supplied to our homes?

19. What can be used to convert one voltage to another?

THE CD REVOLUTION

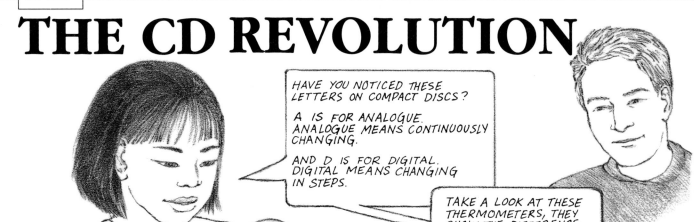

HAVE YOU NOTICED THESE LETTERS ON COMPACT DISCS?

A IS FOR ANALOGUE. ANALOGUE MEANS CONTINUOUSLY CHANGING.

AND D IS FOR DIGITAL. DIGITAL MEANS CHANGING IN STEPS.

TAKE A LOOK AT THESE THERMOMETERS, THEY SHOW THE DIFFERENCE QUITE WELL.

This thermometer is analogue. The volume of mercury inside the bulb expands as the temperature rises, so the level of the mercury in the tube goes up.

Inside the digital thermometer is a thermistor. The electrical resistance of a thermistor changes steadily as the temperature changes, but the electronics in the thermometer makes the display change in steps of 0.1 degrees.

1. What is the temperature reading on: (a) the mercury thermometer (b) the digital thermometer?

2. Which of the changes listed below are: (a) analogue (steady) changes (b) digital (step) changes? the volume of mercury in the thermometer; the resistance of a thermistor; the number of thermometers in a shop; the price of a thermometer; the level of mercury in a thermometer; your temperature; the number shown on a digital thermometer.

ADD

The first letter on a compact disc tells you whether the original recording was analogue or digital.

This graph shows part of the analogue electronic signal from a guitar. The changing sound from the guitar is converted to a changing voltage.

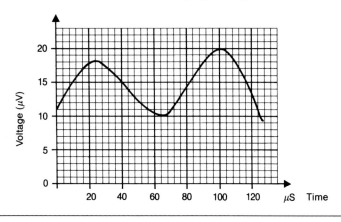

The analogue signal can be recorded, or it can be converted to a digital signal and then stored as a digital recording.

To convert from analogue to digital, the analogue signal is examined approximately every 22 microseconds (44100 times a second!). This is called **sampling**. Here are some results of sampling the guitar signal every 22 microseconds (μS). (μS means microseconds; 1μS is one millionth of one second.)

Time (μS)	0	22	44	66	88	110
Voltage (μV)	11	18		10		18

3. Copy the table and use the graph of the guitar signal to complete it.

4. Plot a bar chart of voltage against time.

WHEN WE LISTEN TO A SAMPLED SIGNAL, SOME OF THE INFORMATION MAY HAVE BEEN THROWN AWAY. WILL WE HEAR A DIFFERENCE?

IT DEPENDS ON HOW OFTEN WE SAMPLE THE SIGNAL.

ADD

We must sample very fast so that the human ear cannot detect the changes. The human ear can hear frequencies up to 20kHz (sounds changing 20 000 times each second). The sampling frequency needs to be at least twice this.

Maximum frequency humans can hear	20kHz
Sampling frequency for Compact Discs	44.1kHz
Maximum frequency dogs can hear	50kHz

5. What sampling frequency would be needed if a CD was produced for dogs?

The guitar sound may be mixed with a number of other sounds and recorded on just one track. The second letter tells you if this track is analogue or digital.

All the voltage values from the sampling process are converted to codes before they are stored. This chart shows how a voltage can be coded into 4 bits:

Any voltage less than 1.5 μV has the code 0000.
A voltage between 1.5 μV and less than 3μV has the code 0001.

For CD's 16 bit codes are used to store sound on the disc.

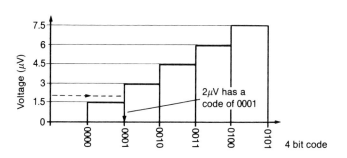

6. Use the chart to find the code for:
(a) 4μV (b) 7.5μV.

ADD

The third letter on the disc is always a D. This tells you that the recording is stored digitally on the disc.

A digital signal is less likely to be affected by unwanted sound (noise) since it is made up only of 0's and 1's. Other values (caused by noise) are ignored by the electronics.

7. What is the advantage of digital recording over analogue recording?

8. Explain what sampling means.

9. Look at the recording information on these five CD's:

(a) Which **must** be incorrect?
(b) Which would you expect to sound most like the original music? Explain your answer.

10. Write an explanation (about 100 words) of the letters on a CD for a teenage magazine.

BY WORD OF MOUTH

From the moment we are born, we can communicate by sound. We make sound by vibrating our vocal cords. As they move backwards and forwards they form layers of both compressed and spread-out air which are called sound waves.

speaker   listener

When these sound waves enter our ears, they make our ear drums and the bones in our ears vibrate. Nerves which can sense these vibrations then carry the information to our brain.

As sound waves travel through air they spread out and the energy they are carrying becomes less concentrated. If the distance between the speaker and the listener is great, the sound waves may be so weak that they cannot be picked up by the listener's ears.

The first invention which allowed people to talk to each other over very long distances was the telephone.

1. Estimate the maximum distance over which you can communicate with a person by shouting.

2. Explain how the ear trumpet, the megaphone, and the empty tin cans on a string shown below can be used to improve communication.

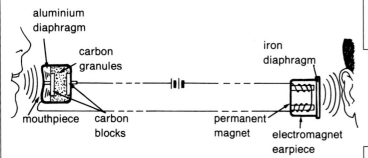

aluminium diaphragm
carbon granules
iron diaphragm
mouthpiece   carbon blocks   permanent magnet   electromagnet earpiece

The handset of a telephone contains a microphone which changes sound waves into electrical pulses. These pulses are carried to a loudspeaker in the receiver, where they reproduce a copy of the original sound which produced the electrical pulses.

Most telephone conversations are carried by sending the electrical pulses through copper wires. Recently, glass fibres have been used to carry the conversations. This is possible because the electrical pulses can be converted to light signals and *vice versa*.

3. Complete this flow chart to show the energy changes which occur in telephones connected by copper wires (or cables).

movement energy in   sound energy
vocal cords ⟶   in speech ⟶

4. Draw out a flow chart to show the energy changes which occur in telephones connected by glass (or optical) fibres.

ADVANTAGES OF USING OPTICAL FIBRES INSTEAD OF COPPER CABLES

A. A bundle of optical fibres will be smaller and lighter than the cable of copper wires that would be needed to do the same job. This makes fibres easier to install.

B. As the signal is carried along a wire or a fibre it gets fainter. The signal can be boosted using a repeater. Signals in glass fibres travel further than signals in copper wires before a repeater is needed.

material	distance before repeater needed
glass fibre	100km
copper wires	4km

C. Glass is made from silica which is commonly found in sand and rocks. Copper is quite scarce. This is one reason why glass fibre could be cheaper than copper wire.

D. It is quite easy to pick up the signal in a copper cable from outside the cable (telephone tapping!). It is not so easy with a light signal inside a fibre, and this means better security.

E. Anything which sparks – like a car engine or a refrigerator switching on or off – can cause interference in the copper cable. Light carried in fibres is not affected.

F. You can carry more conversations in a glass fibre than in a copper cable.

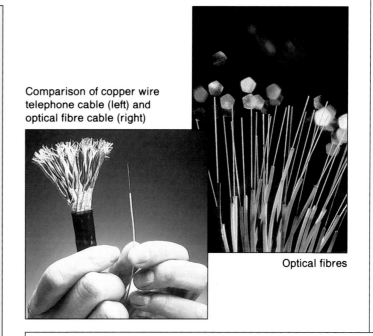

Comparison of copper wire telephone cable (left) and optical fibre cable (right)

Optical fibres

5. Select your three most important reasons for using optical fibres instead of copper cables. List them in order of priority, with the one you think the most important first.

6. The diagram shows the distances between three cities in the UK. Calculate the number of repeaters needed if the telephone lines connecting the cities were made of
   (a) copper cable
   (b) glass fibre.

Newcastle
320km
450km
Birmingham
190km
London

The latest advance in linking telephones over long distances is the use of microwaves and satellites. Microwaves are similar to radiowaves and can be sent around the Earth by satellites.

7. Use the information in the diagram to explain why satellites are necessary to link microwave telephone conversations between distant countries.

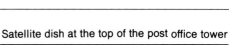

Satellite dish at the top of the post office tower

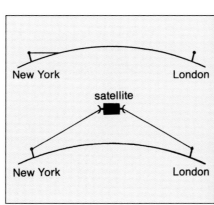

New York   London

satellite

New York   London

A MOVING EXPERIENCE

Ms Green is in charge of four greenhouses used for growing kiwi fruit. To grow the best fruit the plants must not be allowed to dry out or get too hot or too cold. Ms Green is always opening or closing the windows.

I need to set up an electronic circuit to control the windows automatically. They need to be open when the temperature is above 23°C.

1. What are the three parts of an electronic control system?

2. Copy and complete the following description of what the circuit must do:

   The circuit needs to switch on the motor when the temperature reaches ___. It needs to _____ when the window is fully open. Once the temperature falls below ___ again, the motor needs to be switched on in reverse to _____ the window and _____ when it is fully closed.

I think I'll start with a circuit to open the windows. I'll look at the input stage first.

An electronic control system has 3 parts:

INPUT

The input part of the circuit converts the information from the outside world to an electronic signal which the circuit can use. In this case the input information is the temperature of the greenhouse.

PROCESS

The process part takes the input signal, and processes it into the output signal.

When the temperature of a thermistor changes, its resistance changes. We can use a thermistor to convert temperature information into an electronic signal.

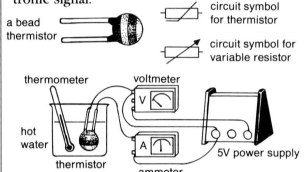

a bead thermistor

circuit symbol for thermistor

circuit symbol for variable resistor

thermometer   voltmeter

hot water

thermistor

ammeter

5V power supply

The thermistor is put into the hot water at a number of different temperatures. Each time the current through the thermistor and the voltage across it are recorded.

Results

Temperature (°C)	Voltage V (V)	Current I (mA)	Resistance of thermistor R (Ω)
10	5	0.17	
15	5	0.22	
20	5	0.27	
25	5	0.33	
30	5	0.41	
40	5	0.61	
50	5	0.83	

The resistance of a thermistor can be calculated using the equation $V = IR$.

3. Draw a circuit diagram for the thermistor test circuit.

4. Copy the table and work out the resistance at each temperature.

5. Plot a graph of resistance against temperature.

6. Copy and complete this statement:
   As the temperature increases the resistance of the thermistor _____.

OUTPUT

The output part of the circuit uses the electronic signal to do the job required. For the greenhouse, the output will be a motor to drive the windows open or closed. The motor needs to be on only while opening or closing the windows.

Ms Green has chosen a 20W motor which needs a 12V power supply.

This is the output circuit:

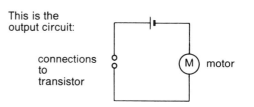

12. Use the equation P = IV (where P is power in watts) to calculate the current which flows in the motor when it is switched on.

Once the window is open the motor will stay on until the greenhouse cools down and the transistor switches off

13. Design a way of using the opening window to switch off the motor.

Ms Green connected up the thermistor in the circuit below with a variable resistor:

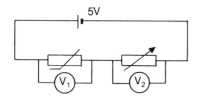

7. Which voltmeter, V₁ or V₂, is measuring the voltage across the thermistor?

8. Use the information in the circuit diagram to complete this equation:

voltage across + voltage across =
thermistor   variable resistor

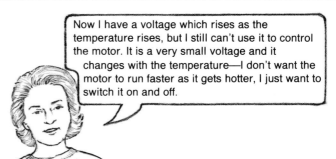

Now I have a voltage which rises as the temperature rises, but I still can't use it to control the motor. It is a very small voltage and it changes with the temperature—I don't want the motor to run faster as it gets hotter, I just want to switch it on and off.

Here are some voltage readings that were taken as the resistance of the thermistor changed:

Resistance of thermistor R (Ω)	Voltage across thermistor V₁	Voltage across variable resistor V₂
18	4.5	
15	4.4	
12	4.2	0.8

Some more electronics must be used to process the signal. A transistor could be used as a switch.

USING A TRANSISTOR AS A SWITCH:

input voltage less than 0.6V	the transistor is switched off
a small input voltage larger than 0.6V	the transistor is switched on, and current will flow in the output circuit

9. Copy and complete the table.

The variable resistor can be adjusted so that the voltage across it reaches 0.6V when the temperature of the thermistor reaches 23°C. This will then switch the motor on at the right temperature.

10. Using your answers to questions 5, 6 and 9, copy and complete the following:
As the temperature rises the voltage across the thermistor _____ and the voltage across the variable resistor _____.

11. Explain how you would do an experiment to find the correct setting for the variable resistor.

KEEPING WARM

Dear Sir

    I received my fuel bill today and am worried about the large amount I owe. I am out of work at present and cannot afford to pay you. Will I be "cut-off" if I do not pay immediately?

    Please can you help me?

            Yours faithfully
            Alan Talbot

Semi-detached house

Dear Mr Talbot

Thank you for your letter. We can be of help in several ways:

1. We can arrange to spread your payments over a period of time to suit yourself. Please come to our local offices and collect the details of our scheme.

2. Have you thought about further insulating your house? There are grant schemes available from some local authorities to help pay for putting insulation in your house. I will send you the address to write to. Anyone can apply.

Did you know that you can lose up to 20% of your heat through your roof, 25% through the walls, 10% through the floor and 20% through the windows, doors and other gaps? That is a great amount of heat to lose and you can save a large amount of money on your fuel bills if you take steps to stop the heating escaping.

Detached house

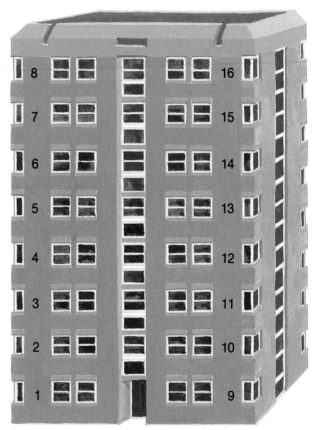

Tower block of flats

1. What is the percentage of heat that Mr Talbot could save if he followed the fuel company's advice?

2. Draw a diagram of your home and show where the various amounts of heat can be lost. Label at least 5 different ways in which heat can be lost.

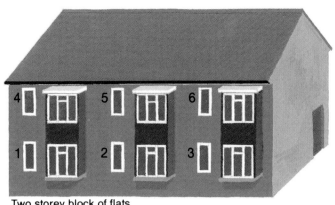
Two storey block of flats

One difference between a semi-detached house and a detached house is that a 'semi' has only 3 outside walls—a detached house has 4 outside walls. Flat number 2 of the two storey block only has 2 outside walls and no outside roof. Walls lose heat by CONDUCTION and RADIATION.

3. Which two types of housing have the least number of outside walls? Give the numbers of the homes with the fewest outside walls.

4. Which types of housing have three outside walls? Write down the number of the homes, and what type of housing they are.

Large windows lose more heat than small ones. Front doors that open on to the street lose more heat than front doors which open inside a large building. In flats, the ceiling of one flat is the floor of the flat above. Heat conducted through the ceilings of the top storey escapes from the roof by CONVECTION (hot air rises). Insulating the roof helps to trap the heat in the rooms below.

5. Where will flat 2 in the tower block gain heat from?

6. What does flat 2 in the two storey block have that flat 2 in the tower block does not have? How will this affect heat losses?

7. Which type of housing is likely to lose most heat through windows?

Floors lose heat by CONDUCTION. A concrete floor will lose more heat by conduction than a wooden one, because concrete is a better conductor than wood. Some concrete floors are now laid on top of a very good insulator made from plastic foam blocks. The problem with wooden floors is that they need some ventilation below them, so that they don't get damp and rot. Carpets help to insulate floors, and underlay beneath the carpet can increase the insulation, as well as making the carpet softer to walk on.

8. Where will flat 3 in the two storey block lose heat? Where will flat 6 gain heat?

9. Which of the terraced houses will lose the least heat? Give a reason for your answer.

10. Draw a diagram of a detached house and mark on it where the house will lose heat by conduction, convection and radiation.

11. If you had a fuel bill for £100, £20 of it could be due to heat lost through the roof. How much money could you be losing through the walls, floors and windows?

Terraced houses

GLOWSAVE VERSUS WONDERWARM

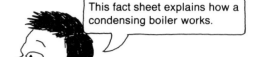

This fact sheet explains how a condensing boiler works.

We are installing gas central heating in our new house.

The question is should we buy an ordinary boiler, or a condensing boiler?

1. What is the process called when hot gases rise?

2. Explain why exhaust gases from a condensing boiler are cooler than from an ordinary boiler.

3. Look at the diagram of the boiler. How are the hot gases made to move downwards through the secondary heat exchanger?

4. What does condensate mean?

5. If you compared a condensing boiler and an ordinary boiler, which boiler would use the least fuel to heat a house? Explain your answer.

We need to know how much each type of boiler costs and how much fuel each one uses.

These leaflets give all the details. Let me know if you have any other questions.

The Glowsave Condensing Boiler

TECHNICAL SPECIFICATION:

Price	£990
Input power	9kW
Output power to water	8kW (8.4kW*)
Heat exchanger material	aluminium
Electrical supply	240V 50Hz
External fuse	3A

*When condensing

The Glowsave boiler has an aluminium heat exchanger. Aluminium is four times more conductive than cast iron.

When the boiler is condensing its efficiency is over 90 per cent. Even when it is not condensing the boiler is more efficient than a ordinary boiler. If Glowsave is compared with an old cast iron boiler the saving in fuel is 40 per cent or more. Even compared to modern cast iron boilers the fuel saving is more than 20 per cent.

The table compares the annual cost of running other central heating boilers with the cost of running the Glowsave boiler:

Type of boiler	Annual cost of gas central heating and hot water/£		
	terraced house	semi-detached house	detached house
15 year old cast iron boiler	303	354	545
new cast iron fanned flue boiler	215	253	389
Glowsave condensing boiler	172	201	310

(the figures are based on 1990 prices, but as prices go up the savings can only get better!)

6. What makes the Glowsave heat exchanger more efficient?

7. Calculate the efficiency of the Glowsave boiler using the fact file
   (a) when it is not condensing
   (b) when it is condensing.

CONDENSING BOILER

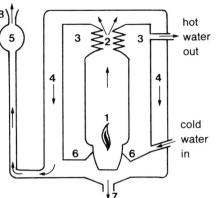

KEY

1. GAS BURNER
2. PRIMARY HEAT EXCHANGER
3. WATER
4. SECONDARY HEAT EXCHANGER
5. EXHAUST GAS FAN
6. COLD WATER ENTERS BOILER
7. CONDENSATE DRAIN
8. EXHAUST GAS FLUE

An ordinary boiler burns gas to heat the water. The waste gases go up the flue and into the atmosphere. Because the waste gases are very hot a lot of heat is wasted.

In a condensing boiler the waste gases are used to heat the water as it returns to the boiler. When the waste gases are eventually released they are much cooler. In fact the water vapour present in the waste gases may have started to condense. This is why the boiler is called a condensing boiler.

The gas burns (1) and the hot gases rise up to the primary heat exchanger (2) by convection. This heats the water (3). The waste gases are drawn into the secondary heat exchanger (4) by the fan (5) and heat the water entering the boiler (6). If the water vapour condenses it is collected in the condensate drain (7). The cooled waste gases pass out of the flue (8).

THE WONDERWARM BOILER

From the outside most boilers look much the same. But how they perform depends on design and quality. This is where the Wonderwarm heat exchanger makes the difference. The exchanger is designed to have more heating fins to increase the surface area and it is made from high quality cast iron. All this makes the boiler more reliable, longer lasting and more efficient.

TECHNICAL SPECIFICATION

Price	£541
Input power	9kW
Output power to water	6.5kW
Heat exchanger material	cast iron
Electrical supply	240V 50Hz
External fuse	3A

Fact file:

Efficiency is a measure of the useful energy output from a system or a machine. It is usually given as a percentage, and calculated like this:

$$\text{efficiency \%} = \frac{\text{useful energy out}}{\text{total energy in}} \times 100$$

The Taylor family live in a detached house with a 15 year old cast iron boiler. They are thinking of buying a condensing boiler.

8. If the price of gas stays the same, how many years will it be before the Taylor family starts to save money?

9. How has the Wonderwarm heat exchanger been made more efficient than older boilers?

10. Calculate the efficiency of the Wonderwarm boiler.

11. Why might people choose a Wonderwarm boiler rather than a more efficient model?

These figures are for an old cast iron boiler:
input power 9kW   output power 4.8kW

12. Calculate the efficiency of the old cast iron boiler.

13. Use all your answers to draw up a table showing types of boilers and their efficiencies.

14. How many years would it be before the Wonderwarm boiler starts to save the Taylor's money, if they buy it instead of the Glowsave boiler?

17 TIDAL ENERGY

Electricity is called a **secondary** source of energy because it first has to be produced from a different or **primary** energy source. A primary source of energy is used to drive a generator. The generator converts this energy into electricity.

Britain generates around 70 per cent of its electricity from coal, 19 per cent from nuclear fuel, 4 per cent from oil and about 2 per cent from hydroelectric power (HEP).

With the exception of hydroelectric power, all these primary sources of energy are non-renewable.

There is a limited supply of each and once they have been used up alternative sources of energy will need to be found.

Many people are concerned at the rate at which we use up non-renewable energy resources. For example, burning fossil fuels is not a very efficient way to obtain energy. It also adds to environmental pollution. One way forward is to generate more electricity from renewable sources of energy, such as solar, wind and tidal power.

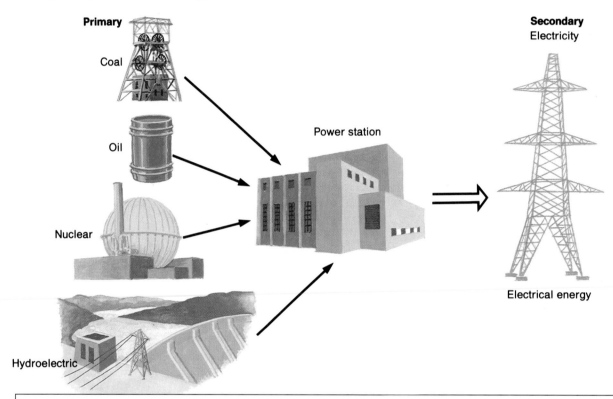

Primary
Coal
Oil
Nuclear
Hydroelectric

Power station

Secondary
Electricity

Electrical energy

For the last 60 years the Severn Estuary has been investigated as a possible site to build a **tidal barrage** to generate electricity.

A tidal barrage is a special type of dam. The barrage is built across a tidal estuary, and allows water to flow up the estuary, but then holds it back. The water is released down the estuary through special turbines built into the barrage. These turbines generate the electricity.

The Severn Estuary is very suitable for this type of dam. Twice a day the tide rises and falls by a number of metres. It has been estimated that such a barrage could supply up to 6 per cent of the United Kingdom's electricity needs by the year 2003.

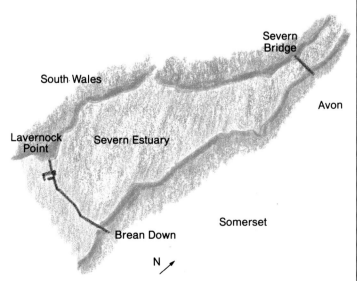

Severn Bridge

South Wales

Avon

Lavernock Point

Severn Estuary

Somerset

Brean Down

N

The Department of Energy has funded £4.2 million towards an investigation to find both the best design for the Severn barrage and the best position to build it. As a result of this a 17km long barrage was proposed, linking Brean Down in Somerset with Lavernock Point in South Wales. The barrage was to have 160 turbines, each with an output of 45 000W. It was estimated that the barrage would take 12 years to build and at 1980 prices, cost £5600 million.

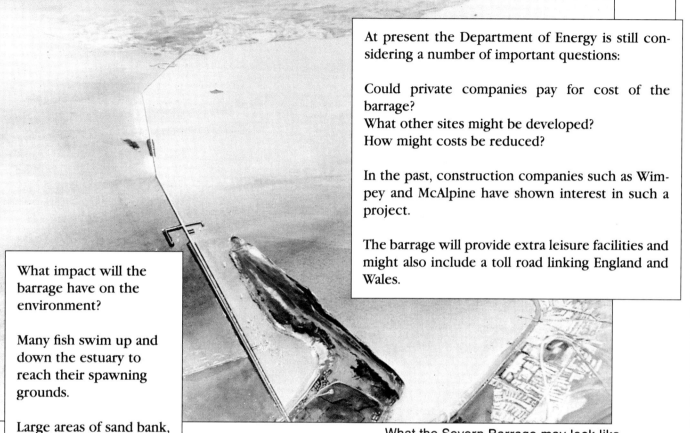

At present the Department of Energy is still considering a number of important questions:

Could private companies pay for cost of the barrage?
What other sites might be developed?
How might costs be reduced?

In the past, construction companies such as Wimpey and McAlpine have shown interest in such a project.

The barrage will provide extra leisure facilities and might also include a toll road linking England and Wales.

What impact will the barrage have on the environment?

Many fish swim up and down the estuary to reach their spawning grounds.

Large areas of sand bank, which provide an ideal habitat for shore birds to live, will be permanently flooded. Often these birds are at the top of an important food chain.

What the Severn Barrage may look like.

YOUR TASK
Write a newspaper article for the "Green Globe". Lay your page out like a newspaper. The headline has been done for you.

In your article you should say:

Why the barrage may be built.
How the barrage will work and the regularity of its electricity supply.
How much electricity the barrage will generate.
What the Department of Energy has done so far.
What the chances are of the barrage being built.
You should also include comments from interviews with a number of people, such as:
A member of the Department of Energy
A member of the Royal Society for the Protection of Birds
A resident of Lavernock
The chairperson of Wimpey.

ROCK GIG

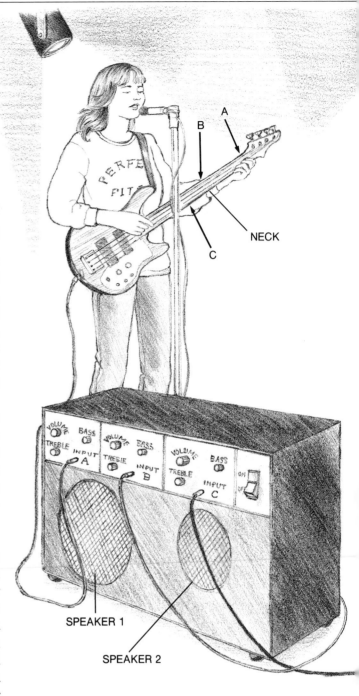

The band were having a practice session, but things weren't going well. "Someone is out of tune" said Jane, who plays bass guitar. "I'll try tightening up the 'E' string to make the pitch higher" said Sean, as he turned the tuning key on his lead guitar. As he altered the pitch of the guitar and the frequency got higher, Alan suddenly said "That's a good note – we could keep it in the number!" "Which note?" asked Jane. "The one that set my snare drum vibrating! It must be a resonance effect – you hit the frequency which is the same as the length of the metal coils under the snare skin."

Later they stopped again at a signal from Jody who was listening at the back of the hall. "I can't hear the harmony from Alan and Jane very well, and the bit on the floor tom-tom is just a muffled rumble. Can't you do anything about it? What about turning up the volume on the mikes a bit and hitting the floor tom-tom harder?"

"The problem is that if we turn up the volume to make us louder, we might drown out the lead vocal from Sean" said Jane. "Well, put some more treble on your voices to give a clearer, high-pitched sound and take some off the bass to remove the low-pitched notes a little – try inputs B and C" said Jody helpfully. "I'm already hitting the floor tom-tom as hard as I can" said Alan. "If I hit the smaller tom-tom the sound will be a higher pitch and probably carry better. The other problem is probably caused by the low pitch of my big cymbal. I'll use the smaller one which is a higher pitch and frequency."

These changes seemed to make the tune sound better, but then there was a setback – Jane's mike stopped working. "It's probably the lead" said Sean. "Wish we had radio mikes. They don't have leads that pack up – the sound is just picked up by the mike, changed into electrical energy, transmitted as radio signals and picked up by a receiver. The electrical energy is then changed back into sound again – the amp makes the electrical signal big enough to drive the speakers." "Boom – boom" went Alan on the bass drum. "Thanks for the physics lesson – but we can't afford them!"

1. The guitarist in the picture plucks the strings with her right hand. Where would the fingers of her left hand have to be placed in order to get a high pitched note? Choose A, B or C.

2. How else could the guitarist change the pitch of the note on the string?

3. Resonance can be a nuisance in a band. Give an example of this effect.

4. Which control would the guitarist have to alter in order to make the sound louder or quieter?

Cymbal 2

Cymbal 1

Floor
tom-tom

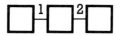
Hihat cymbals

Tom-tom 1

Tom-tom 2

Bass Drum

Snare
drum

FACT FILE

Sound is produced by vibrating objects. The longer a vibrating object, the lower the frequency or pitch. This means that the note will sound lower or more bass. Treble is high pitched, vibrating at a high frequency.

The loudness or volume of a sound depends on how far the vibrating object moves: its amplitude. Volume can be increased by hitting or plucking harder or by increasing the volume on an amplifier – this makes the vibrations in the speakers bigger. Larger speakers respond better to bass notes, and larger cymbals will make lower pitched sounds than smaller ones.

7. (a) Copy the boxes below and fill in the energy changes going on when the guitar is played.

   Guitar – Energy changes

   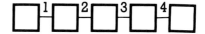

   (b) Devices such as the pick-up on the guitar and the speakers which change energy from one form to another are called **transducers.** Write down which of these transducers is at each of the energy changes 1 and 2.
   (c) What is the purpose of the amplifier?

8. (a) Copy the boxes for the radio mike, and fill in the energy changes which happen when it is used.

   Radio mike – Energy changes

   □—¹□—²□—³□—⁴□

   (b) Name the transducers at positions 1, 2, 3 and 4.

9. Which cymbal on the drum kit would give the lowest pitched sound when hit?

10. What else could Alan do to make the sound of the floor tom-tom carry better?

5. Which input controls would have to be altered to follow Jody's final suggestion?

6. Which of the two speakers do you think would respond best to (a) lower pitched sounds (b) higher pitched sounds?

19
EYE TEST

Hey! Look at Gordon in his new glasses. What's it like? I've got to have them and I'm dreading it!

I didn't want to wear them at first, but it's great being able to see properly. I never knew you could see the bricks in the houses across the street before!

That's funny – I can see things that are far away. It's reading that is my problem. It gives me headaches! So what happened at the optician's?

I sat in the chair and looked at the chart of letters. I could only see the first three!

INFORMATION

When a ray of light goes into or out of a lens it changes direction. This bending of light is called **refraction**.

A converging (convex) lens focuses light:

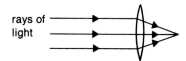

rays of light

A diverging (concave) lens spreads light out:

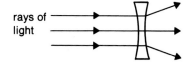

rays of light

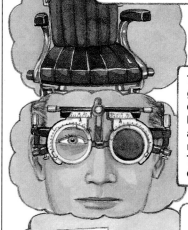

The optician put these glasses on me and covered one eye up. She kept changing the lenses and asking me which made things clearer. Then she did the other eye.

At the end she uncovered both eyes and it was brilliant. I could read it all!

H
AL
TNC
OLHA

Then I chose some frames.

They warned me not to pick really large ones or the lenses would be very thick round the edges.

1. Give two examples of when Gordon's problem – not being able to see things in the distance – might be dangerous.

2. Use the information on these two pages to help you decide what type of lenses Gordon needed.

3. Explain what is meant by **refraction**.

4. Why did the optician test each eye separately?

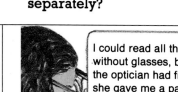

I could read all the chart without glasses, but when the optician had finished she gave me a page of tiny writing to read – with the glasses on it was really clear.

The big frames suited me and the optician said that would be OK with the lenses I need. Large eyes do look attractive and she said these lenses will magnify my eyes.

I wonder why it was so different for each of us at the opticians? I want to know why lenses can help us see more clearly.

5. What type of lenses did Helen need?

6. Give an example of a hobby or pastime which would be difficult if you couldn't see close things clearly.

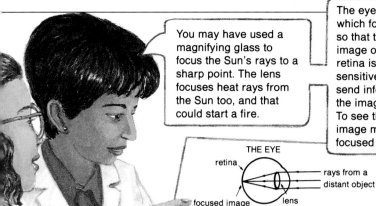

You may have used a magnifying glass to focus the Sun's rays to a sharp point. The lens focuses heat rays from the Sun too, and that could start a fire.

The eye has a lens in it which focuses light rays so that they form an image on the retina. The retina is made of light sensitive cells which send information about the image to the brain. To see things clearly the image must be sharply focused on the retina.

THE EYE

retina

rays from a distant object

focused image   lens

7. Could Gordon use his glasses to focus the Sun's rays? Explain your answer.

8. Could Helen use her glasses to focus the Sun's rays? Explain your answer.

9. What type of lens is in the eye?

10. Using the words retina, lens, and focus, explain why it is dangerous to look directly at the Sun.

If the eyeball is too short or too long the lens doesn't focus the rays sharply on the retina, and vision will be blurred.

SHORT SIGHT

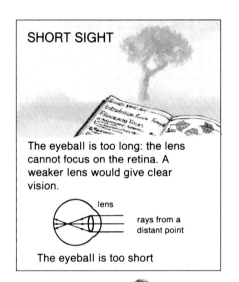

The eyeball is too long: the lens cannot focus on the retina. A weaker lens would give clear vision.

lens

rays from a distant point

The eyeball is too short

LONG SIGHT

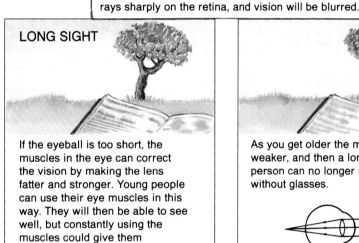

If the eyeball is too short, the muscles in the eye can correct the vision by making the lens fatter and stronger. Young people can use their eye muscles in this way. They will then be able to see well, but constantly using the muscles could give them headaches.

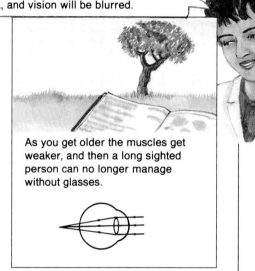

As you get older the muscles get weaker, and then a long sighted person can no longer manage without glasses.

11. What type of lens would spread out the rays in a short-sighted eye so they focused on the retina?

12. What type of lens would make the rays converge more in a long-sighted eye so they focused on the retina?

Gordon's grandfather is also short-sighted. His eye muscles have weakened with age so he needs glasses for close work as well. He uses bifocals – these are lenses in two halves: the top half for seeing distant objects and the bottom half for seeing close objects.

15. Why do you think Gordon's grandfather prefers bifocals to having two pairs of glasses?

Gordon thinks he may choose contact lenses.

13. What type of lens would the top one be?

14. What type of lens would the bottom one be?

16. Which of these contact lenses would be suitable for a short sighted person?

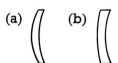

(a)   (b)

COOKING AND DRYING WITH WAVES

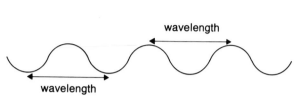

wavelength

wavelength

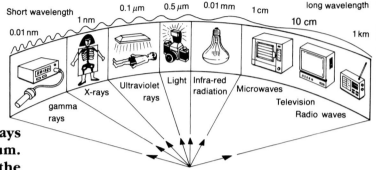

Short wavelength
0.01 nm
1 nm
0.1 μm 0.5 μm 0.01 mm 1 cm
long wavelength
10 cm
1 km

gamma rays
X-rays
Ultraviolet rays
Light
Infra-red radiation
Microwaves
Television
Radio waves

Radio waves, light waves, X-rays and gamma rays are all part of the electromagnetic spectrum. The diagram shows that different parts of the spectrum have different wavelengths.

Electromagnetic waves transfer energy through space – in a vacuum, they travel at about 300 million metres per second. The shorter the wavelength, the more energy the waves can carry.

Microwaves are useful for cooking because the energy they carry is absorbed by the water molecules in food. The more energy the molecules absorb, the more they vibrate and move about. This increase in kinetic energy (energy of movement) means that the food heats up. Microwave cooking is faster than traditional cooking.

Traditional ovens are controlled by thermostats which cut off the supply of electricity to the heater once the correct temperature in the oven has been reached, and turn it on again when the temperature drops. Microwave ovens are controlled by setting the timer and the power output. The power of a microwave oven is measured in watts (W) – that is, the number of joules of electrical energy transformed to microwave energy every second.

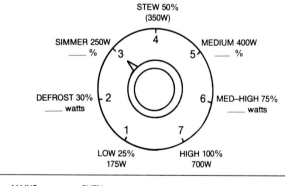

STEW 50%
(350W)
SIMMER 250W
___%
MEDIUM 400W
___%
DEFROST 30%
___ watts
MED–HIGH 75%
___ watts
LOW 25%
175W
HIGH 100%
700W

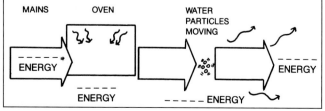

MAINS OVEN WATER PARTICLES MOVING

ENERGY

ENERGY

ENERGY

ENERGY

1. What is the range of wavelengths for microwaves?

2. Which waves in the electromagnetic spectrum can transfer the most energy per second?

3. Suggest why microwaves do not warm up the glass containers which are used to hold food in the oven.

4. Why do manufacturers design microwave ovens so that it is impossible to run them when the door is open?

5. What is the maximum power output of this microwave oven?

6. How many joules of electrical energy are transformed each second if the microwave oven is operating at an output of 50%?

7. Make a copy of the dial on the microwave oven and work out the missing information.

8. Copy out and complete the energy transfer diagram.

Table 1 compares the cost and performance of a traditional steam drier and a radio wave drier.

DIRECT COMPARISON REPORT BETWEEN STEAM AND RADIO DRIERS		
	STEAM	RADIO
DRYING TIME	4–12h	15–45 min
OUTPUT	180kg/h	225kg/h
LOWEST OBTAINABLE MOISTURE CONTENT	22%	10%
START-UP TIME	20 min	3 min
SELLING PRICE OF DRIED MATERIAL	189p/kg	67p/kg
RUNNING COSTS INCLUDING WAGES	£23.60/h	£14.80/h

Table 1

Radio waves are used in some machines to dry textiles before they are dyed.

9. Suggest an explanation for how the drier works.

10. X-ray technicians in hospitals have to wear aprons lined with lead for protection. Explain why the operator of the textile drier does not need similar protection.

During the trial period when the new radio wave drier was being tested, several experiments were carried out to see if it was more efficient at drying batches of cotton than the old steam drier.

Table 2 shows the drying time for 100kg of cotton at a starting moisture of 45% using the radio wave drier.

TEST DATA FOR RADIO WAVE DRIER	
time (mins)	% moisture
0	45
1	45
3	45
5	40
7	36.5
9	32
11	29
13	26.5
15	24.5
17	23
19	21.7
21	20.2

Table 2

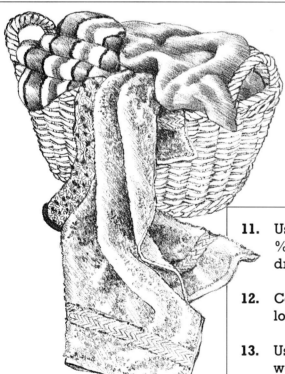

11. Use the information in Table 2 to plot a graph of % moisture against time and find out how long it takes to dry wool from 35% to 25% moisture.

12. Cotton is dried to 14% moisture. If it starts at 27%, how long would this drying process take?

13. Use the data in Table 1 to estimate how many kilograms of wool would be dried in this time by the steam drier.

14. Write a paragraph summarising the advantages of the radio wave drier over the steam drier.

INDEX

Numbers refer to units, not pages.

acceleration 6
ammeter 14
amplifier 18
amplitude 18
analogue scale 12
atoms 3

bimetal strip 2

candles 1
centre of mass 7
Chernobyl 4
compact disc 12
condensing boiler 16
conduction 15
convection 15, 16

diffusion 1
digital scales 12

efficiency 16
electricity
   cost of 8
   units of 8
electric motors 9
electromagnetic spectrum 20
electromagnetism 9
electronic control system 14
energy changes 18
energy source
   primary 17
   secondary 17
equation for power (P = IV) 14
expansion 2
eye 19

fibre optics 13
food irradiation 3
force 5
frequency 12, 18
friction 5

gamma rays 3
gases 1, 2

gas law 10
Geiger counter 4
gravity 5

heat 15
heat exchanger 16
hydroelectric power 17

image 19
insulation 15
interference 13

kilowatt hours 8
kinetic energy 1

lens
   concave 19
   convex 19
liquids 1, 2
loudspeakers 9

magnifying glass 19
mass 5
melting temperature 1
microphone 13
microwaves 20
motor 14

National Grid 11
newtons (N) 5
nuclear fuel 17

particle kinetic theory 2
particles 1
   alpha 3
   beta 3
   in gases 1, 2
   in liquids 1, 2
   in solids 1, 2
pitch 18
power stations
   coal 11
   diesel 11
   gas turbine 11

hydroelectric 11
   nuclear 11
   pumped storage 11
   wind power 11
pressure 10

radiation
   background 4
   heat 15
   ionising 3
radioactive decay 3
radioactivity 3
radio waves 20
refraction 19
resistance 14
retina 19
   resonance 18

sampling 12
satellites 13
Severn Estuary 17
sight
   long 19
   short 19
solids 1, 2
sound 18
   waves 13
speed 6

telephone 13
thermistor 12, 14
thermostat 2
tidal
   barrage 17
   energy 17
transducers 18
transformers 11
transistor 14
treble 18

watts 20
wavelength 20
weight 5

X-rays 4

Acknowledgements

The publishers would like to thank the following for supplying photographs to the units listed:

1 Candle Makers Supplies/David Constable.

3 National Medical Slide Bank.

5 Allsport UK Ltd (athlete, rugby player, tennis player), Cambridge Newspapers Ltd (female cricketers).

7 Allsport UK Ltd (judo players, gymnast, page 15), Eileen Langsley/Supersport (gymnast, page 14), Barnaby's Picture Library (tight rope walker).

9 Amstrad plc (F), Black and Decker (C, L, M, Q, X), Brooker & How Ltd, Hastings (Y), Brooks Plews Associates Ltd, Nottingham (I), Canon (K), Clairol Appliances (O), Dictaphone Ltd (B), Electrolux Domestic Appliances (H), FCA Mavity Ltd, London (G), Hornby Hobbies Ltd (P), Jones and Brothers Ltd, Manchester (D), Moulinex Swan Holdings (A), Neff (UK) Ltd (S), Remington Consumer Products Ltd (N), Sony (UK) Ltd (E, J, R, T, V, W), APV Vent Axia Ltd (U, Z).

13 British Telecommunications plc.

17 Renewable Energy Promotion Group, Harwell.

20 Brooker & How Ltd, Hastings (microwave oven), Strayfield International Ltd (drying equipment).